For Tyler & Naomi Keevil
— happy together!
M.D.

To Abigail, with love
C.U.

Bloomsbury Publishing, London, Berlin, New York and Sydney

First published in Great Britain in May 2011 by Bloomsbury Publishing Plc
36 Soho Square, London, W1D 3QY

Text copyright © Malachy Doyle 2011
Illustrations copyright © Caroline Uff 2011
The moral rights of the author and illustrator have been asserted

A CIP catalogue record of this book is available from the British Library

ISBN 978 0 7475 9548 9

All papers used by Bloomsbury Publishing are natural, recyclable products
made from wood grown in well-managed forests. The manufacturing processes
conform to the environmental regulations of the country of origin

Printed in China by Toppan Leefung Printing Ltd, Dongguang, Guangdong

1 3 5 7 9 10 8 6 4 2

www.bloomsbury.com
www.malachydoyle.com

THE HAPPY BOOK

Malachy Doyle

Illustrated by Caroline Uff

BLOOMSBURY

LONDON BERLIN NEW YORK SYDNEY

Squabble less.

Share more!

Snivel less.

Snuggle more!

Grumble less.

Giggle more!

Goggle less.

Get out more!

Pick less.

Plant more!

Carrots

Shout less.

Sing more!

Grab less.

Give more!

Tease less.

Tickle more!

Sulk less.

Sparkle more!

Worry less.

Wonder more!

Fearless for evermore!

Be strong!

Be happy!